CGP makes starting SATs prep simple!

These Foundation 10-Minute Tests from CGP are perfect for pupils who need some extra help with their KS2 Maths skills. The questions build up to the level of the simplest ones in the SATs.

There's a brilliant range of practice for all the key Arithmetic and Reasoning topics — plus fun puzzle pages throughout the book.

All the answers are at the back, along with a handy progress chart to help keep track of their marks. Everything you need!

What CGP is all about

Our sole aim here at CGP is to produce the highest quality books — carefully written, immaculately presented and dangerously close to being funny.

Then we work our socks off to get them out to you — at the cheapest possible prices.

Contents

Just like in the real tests,
calculators are not allowed.

Published by CGP

Editors: Shaun Harrogate, Sean McParland, Caley Simpson
With thanks to Alison Griffin and Simon Little for the proofreading.

ISBN: 978 1 78908 462 7
Clipart from Corel®
Printed by Elanders Ltd, Newcastle upon Tyne.
Based on the classic CGP style created by Richard Parsons.

There are **9 questions** in this test. Give yourself **10 minutes** to answer them all.

1.   Put these numbers in order from **largest** to **smallest**.

4030   3978   4075

largest		smallest

1 mark

2.   Dana has made the shape below out of 1 cm³ blocks.

    What is the volume of Dana's shape?

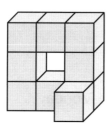

  cm³

1 mark

3.   Write the Roman numeral XXVI as a number.

1 mark

4.　Fill in the missing numbers to make this calculation correct.

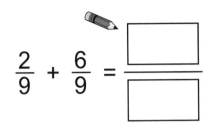

$$\frac{2}{9} + \frac{6}{9} = \frac{\boxed{}}{\boxed{}}$$

1 mark

5.　Carlos draws a pictogram to show the number of watches
he sells on each day of a week.

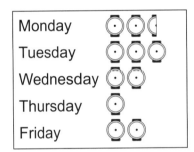

How many watches did Carlos sell on Monday?

1 mark

On which day did Carlos sell the most watches?

1 mark

6. In Wally's toolbox, there are 3 screws for every 2 bolts.

Complete the sentence below.

Wally has 6 screws and [ ] bolts in his toolbox.

1 mark

7. Dana runs for 2 hours each day for 2 weeks.

How many **hours** does she run for in total?

[ ] hours

1 mark

8. A beekeeper gives a formula for how much honey he can make:
Honey (in kg) = Number of beehives × 11

How much honey can be made with 4 beehives?

[ ] kg

1 mark

9. Find two **prime numbers** which multiply to make 21.

A prime number is a number that has exactly two factors: 1 and itself.

[ ] × [ ] = 21

1 mark

END OF TEST

/ 10

There are **8 questions** in this test. Give yourself **10 minutes** to answer them all.

1. Write $1\frac{2}{5}$ as an improper fraction.

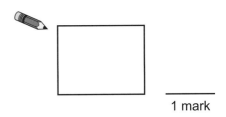

1 mark

2. At a book fair, 924 fiction books and 875 non-fiction books were sold.

What was the total number of books sold at the book fair?

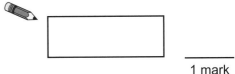

1 mark

3. Circle the larger of the two numbers below.

0.78   0.8

1 mark

4. Circle the value which is equivalent to the weight of the rucksack.

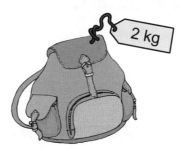

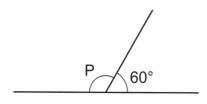 **200 000 grams** **200 grams**

2000 grams **0.2 grams**

_____
1 mark

5. Find the size of angle P in this diagram.

Do not use a protractor (angle measurer).

P 60°

 P = [   ] °

_____
1 mark

6. What is the only **square number** between 10 and 20?

[   ]

_____
1 mark

7. Dana has skied 1 km of a 10 km course.

What **percentage** of the total distance has she covered so far?

%

What **fraction** of the course does she have left to ski?

8. Shape A is a rectangle and Shape B is a square.

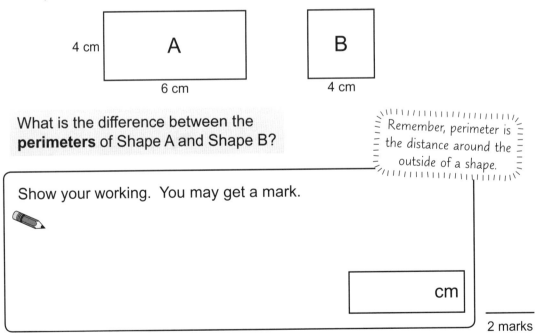

4 cm

A

6 cm

B

4 cm

What is the difference between the **perimeters** of Shape A and Shape B?

Remember, perimeter is the distance around the outside of a shape.

Show your working. You may get a mark.

cm

END OF TEST

/ 10

There are **8 questions** in this test. Give yourself **10 minutes** to answer them all.

1.   Three different types of angle have been drawn below.

Draw lines to match each angle to its name.

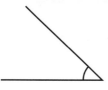

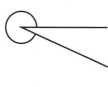

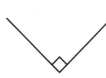

Right
Angle

Reflex
Angle

Acute
Angle

_____

1 mark

None of the angles shown above are obtuse.

Give an example of an obtuse angle.

°

_____

1 mark

2.   Convert $\frac{13}{100}$ into a decimal.

_____

1 mark

7   **Set A**: Test 3

3. The temperature in Glasgow is −3°C.
The temperature in London is 2°C.

How much **warmer** is it in London than in Glasgow?

°C

_____
1 mark

4. The numbers in this sequence increase
by the same amount each time.

Fill in the missing terms.

 5   9 17

_____
1 mark

5. Wally has drawn a net of a shape on the grid below.

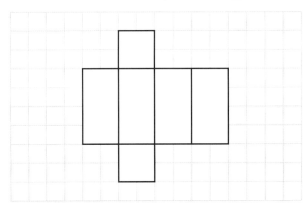

Circle the name of the shape the net makes when it is folded up.

 Cube   Triangular prism

Cuboid   Square-based pyramid

_____
1 mark

---

6. Fill in the boxes to make the three fractions equivalent.

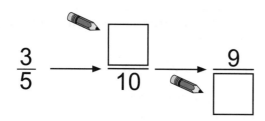

$$\frac{3}{5} \longrightarrow \frac{\boxed{}}{10} \longrightarrow \frac{9}{\boxed{}}$$

_____
1 mark

7. The grid below is made up of 1 cm squares.

    Find the perimeter of the triangle.

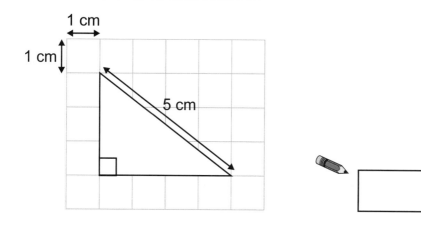

cm

_____
1 mark

8. Carlos has a collection of 120 films.
    10% of his films are action films, and the rest are comedies.

    How many comedy films does he have?

    Show your working. You may get a mark.

    Start by finding the number of his films that are action films, then subtract that from the total.

_____
2 marks

END OF TEST

/ 10

9

Set A: Test 4

There are **8 questions** in this test. Give yourself **10 minutes** to answer them all.

1. Shape A has been drawn on the grid below.

    Draw Shape A after it has been translated
    2 squares to the right and 5 squares down.

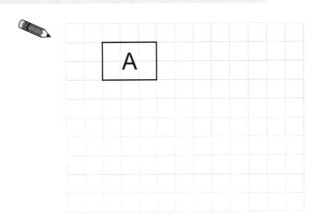

_____
1 mark

2. Circle the correct answer to the sum below.

$$\frac{7}{12} + \frac{10}{12}$$

 $1\frac{4}{12}$ $1\frac{7}{12}$ $2\frac{3}{12}$ $1\frac{5}{12}$

_____
1 mark

3. Fill in the missing digits to make the calculation correct.

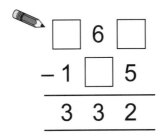

$$\begin{array}{r} \boxed{}\,6\,\boxed{} \\ -\ 1\,\boxed{}\,5 \\ \hline 3\ \ 3\ \ 2 \end{array}$$

_____
1 mark

4. A pet shop sells a selection of items:

Dog Bowl £6.50   **Pug Mug** £3.95   **Tennis Ball** £0.45

What is the total cost of one dog bowl and one pug mug?

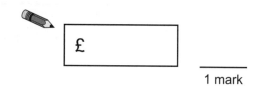

£

1 mark

How much **more** does a dog bowl cost than a tennis ball?

£

1 mark

5. A rectangular carpet has a length of 9 m and a width of 7 m.

What is the area of the carpet?

Area of a rectangle = length × width

m²

1 mark

6. Wally caught 10 fish on a fishing trip. 7 of the fish were cod.

What **percentage** of the fish that he caught were cod?

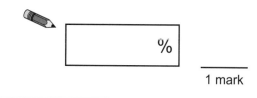

%

1 mark

7.   25 people play in a band. The table below shows
      how many people play each type of instrument.

Type of instrument	Number of players
Woodwind	11
Percussion	6
Brass	8

How many people in the band **don't** play a woodwind instrument?

_____
1 mark

8.   6 mugs can hold the same amount of liquid
      as 2 bottles.
      One mug can hold 400 ml.

      How much can one bottle hold?

Show your working. You may get a mark.

ml

_____
2 marks

END OF TEST

/ 10

There are **8 questions** in this test. Give yourself **10 minutes** to answer them all.

1.   The distance to a golf course is shown on the signpost below.

How many **kilometres** is it from the signpost to the golf course?

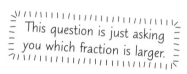 km

2.   Each weight below weighs a fraction of 1 kg.

Circle the weight which is **heavier**.

This question is just asking you which fraction is larger.

3.   Work out the volume of the cuboid below.

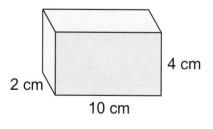

4 cm

2 cm

10 cm

 cm^3

4. A machine in a factory makes toy cars.
   The machine makes 471 cars each day.

   How many cars does it make in 6 days?

   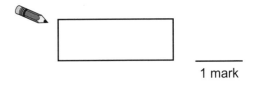

   _____
   1 mark

5. Fill in the missing numbers to make this calculation correct.

   $$\frac{3}{4} \times \frac{1}{2} = \frac{\boxed{}}{\boxed{}}$$

   _____
   1 mark

6. A rectangle is drawn on the set of axes below.

   Find the coordinates of point P.

   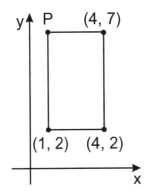

   P = (_____ , _____)

   _____
   1 mark

7. Dana works in an ice cream van. The formula for how much money she earns in one day is: Money earned = £2 × ice creams sold + £8.

Dana sells 16 ice creams on Monday.

How much money does she earn on Monday?

£ [   ]

_____
1 mark

Dana saves $\frac{3}{4}$ of her earnings each day.

How much does she save on Monday?

£ [   ]

_____
1 mark

8. The shape on the right is made up of a rectangle and a triangle.

Calculate the area of the shape.

6 m

4 m

6 m   2 m

Split up the shape and work out the areas of the rectangle and triangle separately. The formula for the area of a triangle is $\frac{1}{2}$ × base × height.

Show your working. You may get a mark.

[   ] m²

_____
2 marks

END OF TEST

[   ] / 10

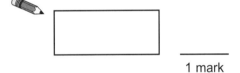
There are **8 questions** in this test. Give yourself **10 minutes** to answer them all.
Show your working in the spaces and write your answers in the boxes.

1. 351 – 100

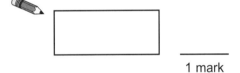

_____
1 mark

2. 14 ÷ 1

_____
1 mark

3. 1923 – 1002

_____
1 mark

4. 3 × 4 × 5

_____
1 mark

5. $\dfrac{1}{7} \times \dfrac{1}{5}$

1 mark

6. 20% of 400

1 mark

7.
```
  1 5 9
×     4
```

2 marks

8. 9 ⟌ 6 1 2

2 marks

END OF TEST

/ 10

Shape Search

Find the **seven** shape words in the wordsearch below, then use them to fill in the sentences at the bottom of the page. The description for one of the words is missing, so you'll have to write your own.

I	S	O	S	C	E	L	E	S	P	Y	O	R
C	I	R	C	U	M	F	E	R	E	N	C	E
O	R	E	H	X	A	N	U	T	N	E	T	S
S	T	G	J	E	F	O	Z	J	T	K	A	R
V	E	U	Y	S	E	N	A	L	A	W	G	K
A	U	L	R	Q	R	I	E	P	G	U	O	A
D	G	A	T	H	E	X	A	G	O	N	N	I
P	A	R	A	L	L	E	L	M	N	S	C	R

1. A .... is a six-sided shape.

2. .... lines are the same distance apart and never meet.

3. .... polygons have equal-length sides and equal angles.

4. The .... is the outside edge of a circle.

5. .... triangles have two equal sides and two equal angles.

6. A shape with five sides is called a ....

7. ....

....

End of Set A: Scoresheet

You've finished a full set of tests — well done!

Now it's time to put your scores in here
and see how you're getting on.

	Score	
Test 1		/10
Test 2		/10
Test 3		/10
Test 4		/10
Test 5		/10
Arithmetic Test		/10
Total		**/60**

Once you've got a score out of 60, check it out in the table below...

0 – 29	If you got a lot of questions wrong, don't worry. **Practise** the topics you struggled with, then **have another go** at **this** set of tests.
30 – 45	If you got half-marks or better, you're doing well. Look back through the questions you got wrong and **brush up** on those topics. Then try the **next set** of tests.
46 – 60	Woohoo! Now have a go at the **next set** of tests — can you beat your score?

There are **9 questions** in this test. Give yourself **10 minutes** to answer them all.

1.   Write the number 27 409 in words.

_____
1 mark

2.   The rectangle below has been divided into equal sections.

Shade in $\frac{1}{3}$ of the rectangle.

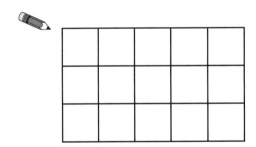

_____
1 mark

3.   Round each of these amounts to the **nearest £10**.

£892 ⟶ 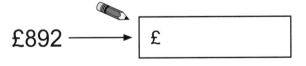 £

£1736 ⟶ 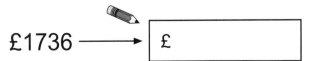 £

_____
1 mark

4.   Part of a shape is drawn on the grid below.

Complete the shape so that it has an area of 10 cm².

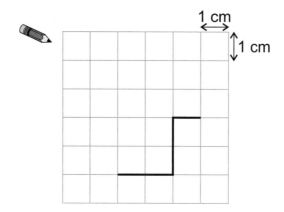

1 cm

1 cm

5.   Circle all the numbers below that are multiples of 3.

15   11   9

5   12   8

6.   Customers at a cafe choose two different items off the menu.
The choices on the menu are a sandwich, soup, a salad or chips.

What **two** possible combinations are missing from the list below?

Sandwich   and   soup

Sandwich   and   salad

Sandwich   and   chips

Soup   and   salad

[   ]   and   [   ]

[   ]   and   [   ]

7. Find the missing angle x in the diagram.

Do not use a protractor (angle measurer).

Angles around a point add up to 360°.

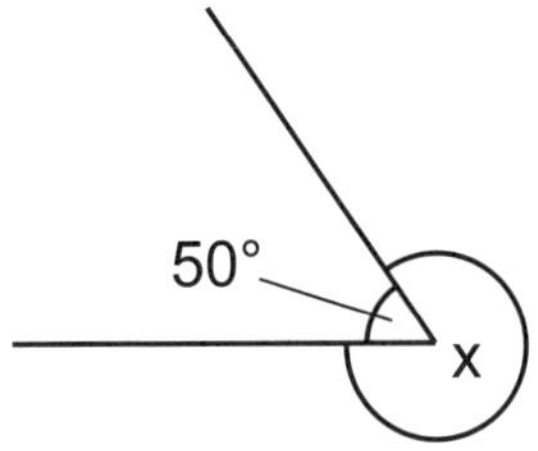

50°

x

x = [   ] °

_____
1 mark

8. 5% of the children in Jon's school are going on a trip.
There are 200 children at his school.

Circle the option that shows how many children are going on the trip.

20   5   10   9   7

_____
1 mark

9. 1 cm on a map represents 10 km in real life.

If two towns are 5 cm apart on the map,
how far apart are they in real life?

[   ] km

_____
1 mark

Two lakes are 20 km apart in real life.

How far apart are they on the map?

[   ] cm

_____
1 mark

END OF TEST

[/ 10   ]

Set B: Test 1   22   © CGP — not to be photocopied

There are **7 questions** in this test. Give yourself **10 minutes** to answer them all.

1. Abe is writing a story. He writes 2260 words on Monday.
    He writes 1000 words on Tuesday.

    How many words has Abe written by the end of Tuesday?

    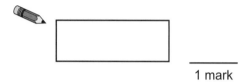

    _____
    1 mark

2. The boat below is made up of three shapes:
    a rectangle, a parallelogram and a trapezium.

    Which part of the boat is a trapezium? Circle the correct letter.

    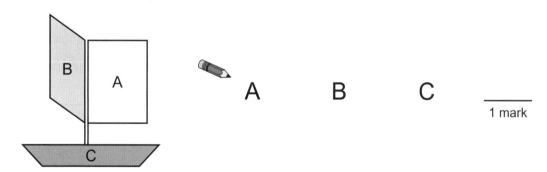

    A   B   C   _____
    1 mark

    There is also a flag on the boat. The flag is an isosceles triangle.

    Complete the flag on the grid below.

    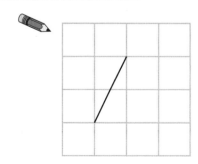

    _____
    1 mark

---

3.   Circle the net which could fold to make a cube.

     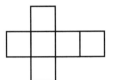

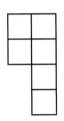   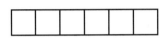

_____

1 mark

4.   Farrah has written on $\frac{1}{20}$ of the pages in her diary.

Write this fraction as a decimal.

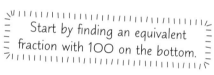

Start by finding an equivalent
fraction with 100 on the bottom.

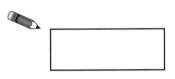

_____

1 mark

5.   Find the missing angle A in the diagram below.

Do not use a protractor (angle measurer).

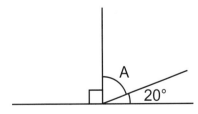

A =   °

_____

1 mark

6. Round each number below to the nearest whole number.

70.3 → [   ]   9.9 → [   ]

1 mark

Use your rounded numbers to estimate the answer to 70.3 ÷ 9.9.

4   12   9   7

1 mark

7. Calculate the mean of the numbers listed below.

4   6   11   7

Show your working. You may get a mark.

[   ]

2 marks

END OF TEST

[   ] / 10

Set B: Test 3

There are **8 questions** in this test. Give yourself **10 minutes** to answer them all.

1.   Draw lines to match each shape to one of its properties.

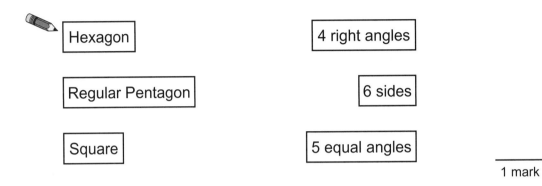

Hexagon		4 right angles
Regular Pentagon		6 sides
Square		5 equal angles

_____
1 mark

2.   Part of a shape has been drawn on the grid below.

Finish the shape to make it symmetrical about the mirror line.

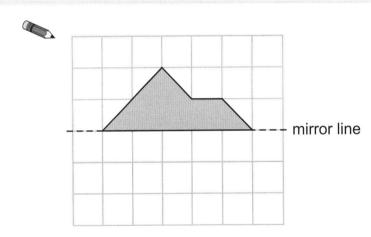

mirror line

_____
1 mark

3.   4 kg of wool can make 60 pairs of socks.

How many pairs of socks can be made with 12 kg of wool?

_____
1 mark

4.   Look at this tram timetable.

Neeston	06:10	09:20	10:15	12:40
Lowbury	06:50	10:00	10:55	13:20
Bullwall	07:00	10:10	11:05	13:30

Farrah is going from Lowbury to Bullwall.

What time is the **latest** tram she can catch from
Lowbury if she wants to get to Bullwall before 11:00?

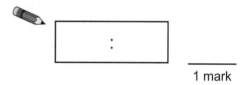

_____

1 mark

5.   Circle the calculation that **does not** equal 10.

Remember to do the
bit in brackets first.

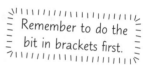 4 × 3 − 2   2 + 3 × 2   (15 + 5) ÷ 2

_____

1 mark

6.   800 roses are divided into bunches of 6.

How many **whole** bunches of roses are there?

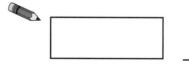

_____

1 mark

How many **more** roses are needed to make another bunch?

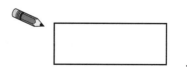

_____

1 mark

7. Abe has three cards with fractions written on them.

$$\frac{1}{3} \quad \frac{5}{12} \quad \frac{1}{6}$$

Write the fractions in order from **smallest** to **largest**.

smallest		largest

1 mark

8. A cafe's menu is shown on the right.
Jon orders 2 coffees and 3 slices of cake.
He has a £5 note.

Coffee	£2.10
Cake	£1.50
Soup	£3.25

How much **more** money does
Jon need to pay for his order?

Show your working. You may get a mark.

£

2 marks

END OF TEST

/ 10

There are **8 questions** in this test. Give yourself **10 minutes** to answer them all.

1.　　Calculate 72.6 – 10

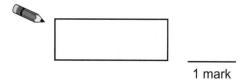

1 mark

2.　　In Class 5B, each child takes part in one after-school activity.
　　　The bar chart shows how many children take part in each activity.

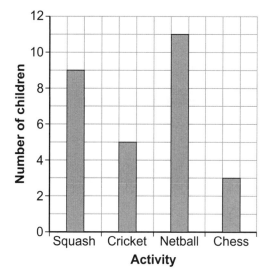

How many children in Class 5B play cricket?

1 mark

How many children are there in Class 5B?

1 mark

3. This clock shows a time in the **evening**.

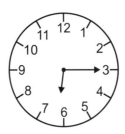

Write the time the clock will show **in one hour** using the 24-hour clock.

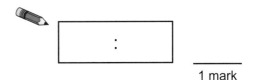

_____
1 mark

4. Circle the numbers in the list below that are factors of 20.

  3   4   5   8   10

_____
1 mark

5. Abe's dad will be 47 in 5 years' time. Abe is half his dad's age now.

How old is Abe now?

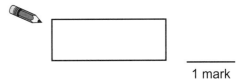

_____
1 mark

6. In a forest, there are only birch trees and oak trees.
For every 1 birch tree there are 3 oak trees.

What **fraction** of the trees in the forest are birch trees?

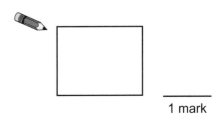

_____
1 mark

7. Shape Y has been
    translated to give Shape Z.

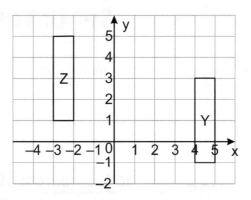

Describe the translation by filling in the boxes
and circling the correct directions.

Shape Y has been translated ☐ units to the left / right

and ☐ units up / down.

_____

1 mark

8. Abe and Farrah are competing in a canoe race.

    Abe is $\frac{26}{50}$ through the race and Farrah is 62% through the race.

    Who is **further ahead**?

Start by converting the
fraction to a percentage.

    Show your working. You may get a mark.

    ☐

_____

2 marks

END OF TEST

☐ / 10

There are **7 questions** in this test. Give yourself **10 minutes** to answer them all.

1.   Round each of these numbers.

265   — to the nearest **100** →   [ ]

18 910   — to the nearest **1000** →   [ ]

2.   There are 40 flowers in a garden.
The pie chart below shows the different types of flowers in the garden.

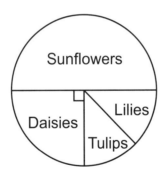

Using the pie chart, circle the statements below that are **true**.

   There are twice as many daisies as lilies.

There are more than 20 tulips.

Three-quarters of the flowers are sunflowers.

There are the same number of tulips and lilies.

2 marks

3.   Fill in the missing number in the calculation below.

$$2.63 \times \boxed{} = 263$$

_____
1 mark

4.   Find the size of the missing angle in this right-angled triangle.

Do not use a protractor (angle measurer).

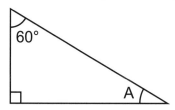

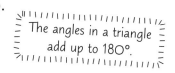

The angles in a triangle add up to 180°.

$A = \boxed{}$ °

_____
1 mark

5.   Farrah has 60 grapes. She gives away $\frac{1}{3}$ of her grapes.
She shares these grapes equally between four of her friends.

How many grapes does each friend get?

_____
1 mark

6.   A cube has sides of 3 cm.
     A cuboid has a volume of 24 cm³.

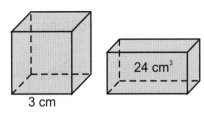

     What is the difference between the volumes of the two shapes?

     Show your working. You may get a mark.

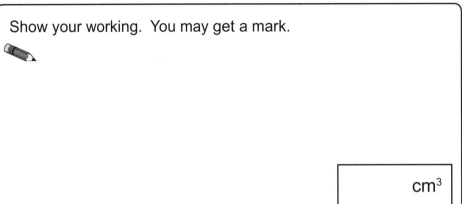

     [ ] cm³

7.   Farrah has a 1-litre bottle of orange juice.
     She pours $\frac{2}{5}$ of a litre into a jug and $\frac{3}{10}$ of a litre into a glass.

     What fraction of a litre of orange juice is left in the bottle?

     Show your working. You may get a mark.

     [ ] litre

END OF TEST

[ ]   / 10

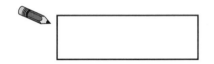
There are **8 questions** in this test. Give yourself **10 minutes** to answer them all.
Show your working in the spaces and write your answers in the boxes.

1. 9032 + 2000

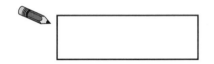

1 mark

2. 18 × 5

1 mark

3. $\frac{4}{6} + \frac{1}{6}$

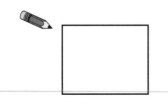

1 mark

4. 36.5 × 10

1 mark

---

5. $\frac{1}{8}$ of 32

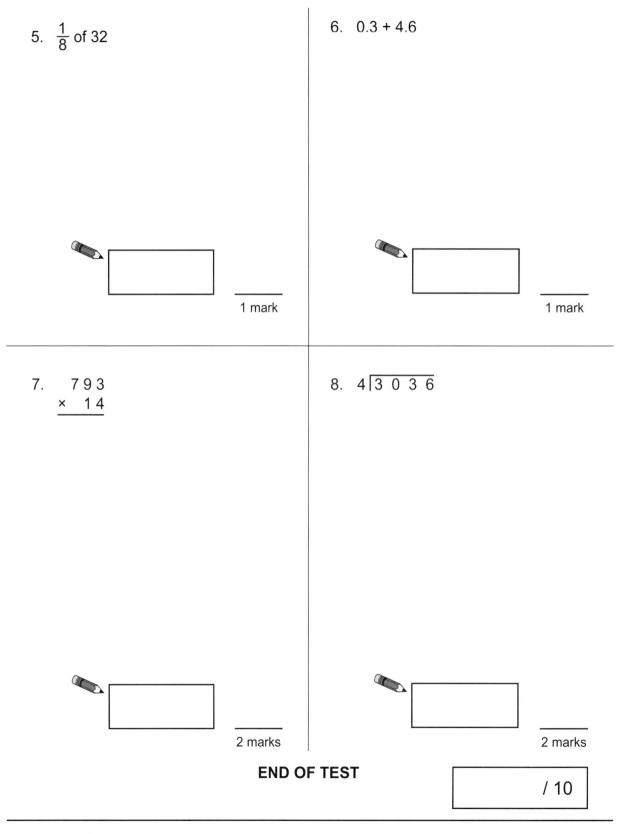

_____
1 mark

6. 0.3 + 4.6

_____
1 mark

7.   7 9 3
  ×   1 4
  ―――――

_____
2 marks

8. 4 ⟌ 3 0 3 6

_____
2 marks

END OF TEST

| / 10 |

Computer Conundrum

Peter and Yasmin are playing a computer game. They have to get their players through Mal's Evil Lair by solving the calculations in the doorways. Their final score is the sum of the answers to these calculations.
They get a prize based on their final score, as shown in the table below.

Score	0-50	51-100	101-150	151-200
Prize	Healing potion	Magic sword	Skeleton key	Fairy wand

What prizes do Peter and Yasmin get?

Peter

$81 \div 9$

6×12

7×8

$32 \div 4$

☐ + ☐ + ☐ + ☐ = ☐

Yasmin

9×7

$54 \div 6$

$66 \div 11$

8×12

☐ + ☐ + ☐ + ☐ = ☐

Peter's prize: ....   Yasmin's prize: ....

End of Set B: Scoresheet

You've finished a full set of tests — well done!

Now it's time to put your scores in here
and see how you're getting on.

	Score	
Test 1		/10
Test 2		/10
Test 3		/10
Test 4		/10
Test 5		/10
Arithmetic Test		/10
Total		**/60**

Once you've got a score out of 60, check it out in the table below...

0 – 29	If you got a lot of questions wrong, don't worry. **Practise** the topics you struggled with, then **have another go** at **this** set of tests.
30 – 45	If you got half-marks or better, you're doing well. Look back through the questions you got wrong and **brush up** on those topics. Then try the **next set** of tests.
46 – 60	Woohoo! Now have a go at the **next set** of tests — can you beat your score?

There are **9 questions** in this test. Give yourself **10 minutes** to answer them all.

1. Write < or > in each box to make these number sentences correct.

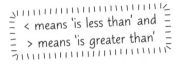
< means 'is less than' and
> means 'is greater than'

 188 ☐ 181

3921 ☐ 3995

———
1 mark

2. Hiro put some water in this kettle.

How much water is in the kettle?

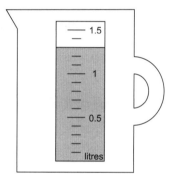

☐ litres

———
1 mark

3. Isla has drawn three triangles below.

Draw lines to match each triangle with its correct name.

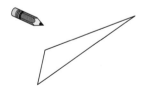

| scalene triangle | equilateral triangle | isosceles triangle |

———
1 mark

39

4. The temperature in a fridge is 1 °C.
The temperature in a freezer is –8 °C.

What is the **difference** in temperature
between the fridge and the freezer?

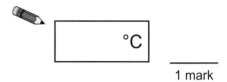

°C

_____
1 mark

5. A recipe says to bake a cake for 15 minutes.
Leanne has baked her cake for 12 minutes 40 seconds.

How much longer does she need to bake her cake for?

mins   seconds

_____
1 mark

6. Circle the two shapes on the grid below that have the **same area**.

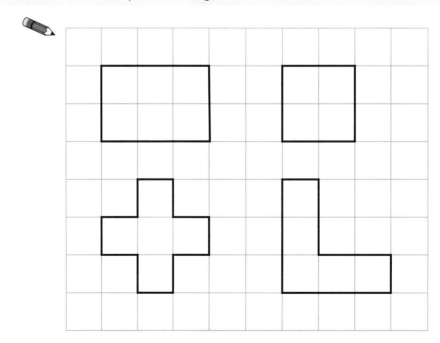

_____
1 mark

7. Write $\frac{19}{7}$ as a mixed number.

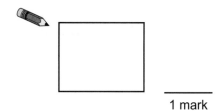

_____
1 mark

8. Reflect shape S in the y-axis.

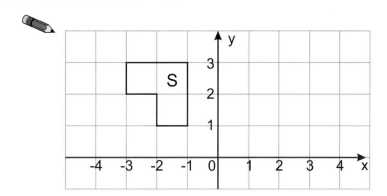

_____
1 mark

9. Hiro pays £2.99 for 60 text messages.
Isla pays 4p for each text message she sends.

How much **more** does Hiro pay
if they both send 60 text messages?

Show your working. You may get a mark.

p

_____
2 marks

END OF TEST

/ 10

41

Set C: Test 1

There are **8 questions** in this test. Give yourself **10 minutes** to answer them all.

1. Write down the coordinates of the points marked on the shape below.

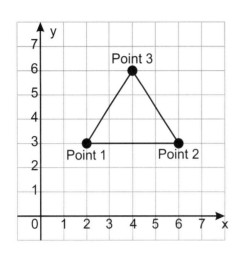

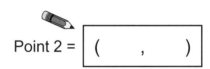

Point 1 = (,)

Point 2 = (,)

Point 3 = (,)

_____
1 mark

2. Isla runs 0.65 km and Leanne runs 680 m.

Who runs further?

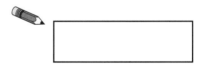

_____
1 mark

3. The table below shows the cost of theme park attractions.

	Dodgems	Ferris Wheel	Log Flume
Child	£1	£4	£2
Adult	£2	£5	£3

5 children go on the Log Flume and 3 adults go on the Ferris Wheel.

What is the total cost?

£

_____
1 mark

4. Leanne calculates that 98 × 13 = 1274.

Write a division she could do to check her answer.

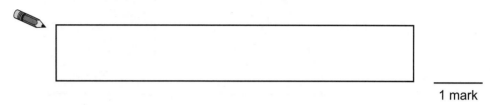

_____
1 mark

5. Hiro uses 20 ml of squash to make a drink.

How many drinks can he make from a 0.5 litre bottle of squash?

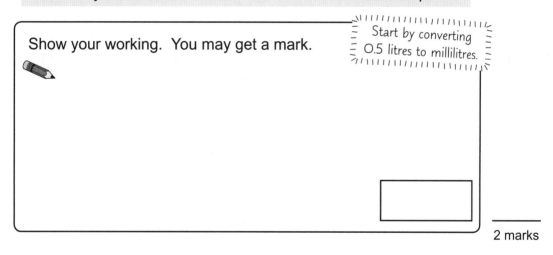

Show your working. You may get a mark.

Start by converting 0.5 litres to millilitres.

_____
2 marks

6. 25% of customers at a hairdressers have blonde hair.

What **fraction** of customers **don't** have blonde hair?

Give your answer in its simplest form.

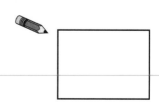

_____
1 mark

7. Find the **difference** in area between the triangle and square below.

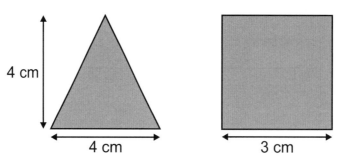

4 cm

4 cm

3 cm

Show your working. You may get a mark.

cm²

8. Find the whole-number values for A and B that make both of these calculations true.

Start by finding the pairs of numbers that multiply to give 12, then see which pair adds up to 8.

$$A × B = 12 \qquad A + B = 8$$

A =

B =

END OF TEST

/ 10

There are **8 questions** in this test. Give yourself **10 minutes** to answer them all.

1. The diameter of this circle is 6 mm.

    What is the radius of the circle?

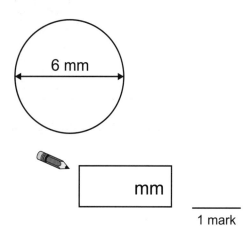

    6 mm

    | mm |

    _____
    1 mark

2. An aeroplane has a wingspan of 58.6 m.

    What is the wingspan to the nearest whole metre?

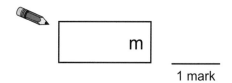

    | m |

    _____
    1 mark

3. 1740 people watch a cricket match.
    On average, each person spends £12 on food during the match.

    What is the total amount of money spent on food during the match?

    Show your working. You may get a mark.

    £

    _____
    2 marks

4. Isla, Hiro and Leanne are playing a board game.
The pictogram shows how many points they each have.

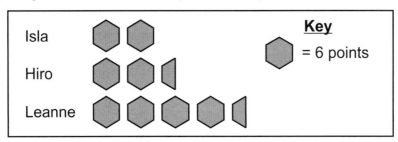

How many **more** points does Leanne have than Isla?

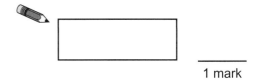

1 mark

5. Leanne has read $\frac{3}{5}$ of a 40-page book.

How many pages has Leanne read?

1 mark

6. There are 300 fossils on display in a museum.
60% of the fossils are dinosaur fossils.

How many fossils are dinosaur fossils?

1 mark

7. 8 kilometres equals 5 miles.
   Isla drives 30 miles to get to her parents' house.

   How many kilometres does Isla drive?

   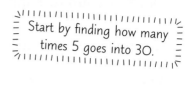
   Start by finding how many times 5 goes into 30.

   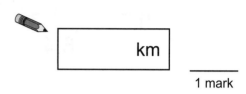

   | km |

   _____
   1 mark

8. An artist takes 6 hours in total to complete a painting.
   The artist paints for 10 minutes each day.

   How many days does it take the
   artist to complete the painting?

   Show your working. You may get a mark.

   | days |

   _____
   2 marks

END OF TEST

| / 10 |

Set C: Test 3

There are **7 questions** in this test. Give yourself **10 minutes** to answer them all.

1. Circle **two** of the numbers below that add to make 10.

9.7   1.2   3.6   6.4   1.3

_____
1 mark

2. Use a protractor (angle measurer) to measure angle A in this diagram.

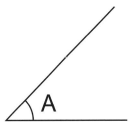

A = [   ] °

_____
1 mark

3. A ferry ticket costs £3.20.

   Work out the total cost of 300 ferry tickets.

£ [   ]

_____
1 mark

   Leanne buys 3 ferry tickets with a £10 note.

   How much change does Leanne get?

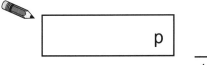

[   ] p

_____
1 mark

4.   The Roman numerals on the side of this
     ship show the year that it was built.

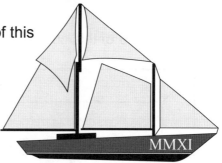

Write the year that the ship was built as a number.

_____
1 mark

5.   A shape has been drawn on a grid.
     The shape is translated 4 squares to the left and 3 squares down.

Draw the translated shape on the grid below.

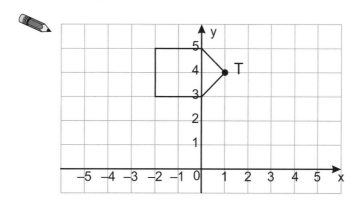

_____
1 mark

What are the coordinates of point T on your translated shape?

T = (,   )

_____
1 mark

49   **Set C**: Test 4

6. Find the volume of this cuboid.

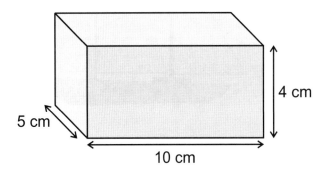

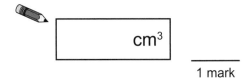

7. Isla has 5 identical apples and cuts each one into 6 slices.
She gives 9 slices to her rabbit.

How many apples does she have left?

Give your answer as a mixed number in its simplest form.

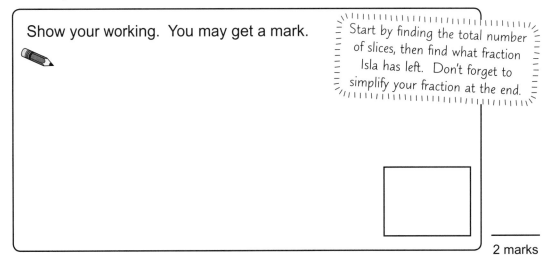

Show your working. You may get a mark.

Start by finding the total number of slices, then find what fraction Isla has left. Don't forget to simplify your fraction at the end.

2 marks

END OF TEST

/ 10

There are **8 questions** in this test. Give yourself **10 minutes** to answer them all.

1. Look at this box of shapes and complete the sentence below.

For every pentagon there are ☐ triangles.

_____
1 mark

2. The numbers in the sequence below decrease by 8 each time.

Fill in the missing numbers.

 ☐   22   14   ☐   ☐

_____
1 mark

3. Hiro has 5275 pens to divide into boxes.

How many whole boxes can he fill if one box can hold 25 pens?

Show your working. You may get a mark.

_____
2 marks

4.   Look at this 3D shape.

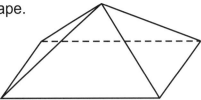

Fill in the table for this shape.

Number of faces	Number of edges	Number of vertices

5.   The line graph below shows the length of a bus journey against the cost of a ticket.

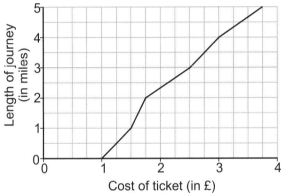

Work out the cost of a ticket for a 3 mile journey.

£

6.   Circle the numbers in the list below that are **common multiples** of 3 and 5.

5   9   15   24   30

7. The diagram shows Leanne's garden.
A hedge goes around the perimeter of her garden.

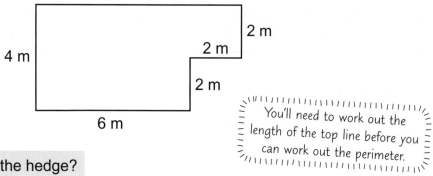

4 m

2 m

2 m

2 m

6 m

How long is the hedge?

You'll need to work out the length of the top line before you can work out the perimeter.

[ ] m

_____
1 mark

8. Find **all** the possible pairs of positive whole-number values for ◯ and ▽.

$$3 \times \bigcirc + \triangledown = 13$$

	◯	▽
Pair 1		10
Pair 2	2	
Pair 3	3	
Pair 4		1

_____
2 marks

END OF TEST

/ 10

There are **8 questions** in this test. Give yourself **10 minutes** to answer them all.
Show your working in the spaces and write your answers in the boxes.

1. 2000 + 600 + 30

1 mark

2. 18.5 – 8.3

1 mark

3. 5^2

1 mark

4. 490 ÷ 7

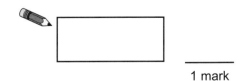

1 mark

5. $\dfrac{4}{5} \div 3$

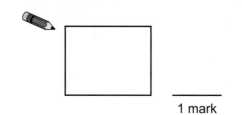

1 mark

6. $\dfrac{1}{14} + \dfrac{2}{7}$

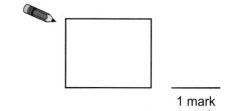

1 mark

7.
```
    2 7 3 1
  ×     2 2
```

2 marks

8. $12\overline{)4\ 9\ 9\ 2}$

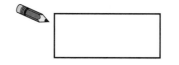

2 marks

END OF TEST

/ 10

Trek to the Temple

Thuli is on an adventure in the jungle. She has to get to the
Legendary Diamond at the centre of the Secret Temple at exactly midnight.
The list below shows the different tasks she has to do and how long they will take.

1. Finding the Hidden Compass — 0.5 hours

2. Swimming the Rapid River — 45 minutes

3. Escaping the Cursed Quicksand — 2 hours

4. Swinging across the Perilous Vines — $1\frac{1}{4}$ hours

5. Hiking the Holy Hill — 3 hours

6. Dodging traps in the Secret Temple — 1 hour 30 minutes

> Thuli can start the next task as soon as she's finished the previous one.

Fill in the timetable to work out what time Thuli needs
to start each task to get to the diamond on time.
Start from midnight (00:00) and work **backwards**.
Use the 24-hour clock.

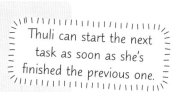

	Start Time	End Time
Hidden Compass		
Rapid River		
Cursed Quicksand		
Perilous Vines		
Holy Hill		
Secret Temple		Midnight

End of Set C: Scoresheet

You've finished a full set of tests — well done!

Now it's time to put your scores in here
and see how you're getting on.

	Score	
Test 1		/10
Test 2		/10
Test 3		/10
Test 4		/10
Test 5		/10
Arithmetic Test		/10
Total		**/60**

Once you've got a score out of 60, check it out in the table below...

0 – 29	If you got a lot of questions wrong, don't worry. **Practise** the topics you struggled with, then **have another go** at **this** set of tests.
30 – 45	If you got half-marks or better, you're doing well. Look back through the questions you got wrong and **brush up** on those topics until you're happy with them.
46 – 60	Woohoo! You've done really well — congratulations.

Answers

Set A

Test 1 – pages 1-3

1. 4075, 4030, 3978
   (**1 mark for correct order**)

2. 9 cm³ (**1 mark**)

3. 26 (**1 mark**)

4. $\frac{2}{9} + \frac{6}{9} = \frac{8}{9}$ (**1 mark**)

5. 1 watch symbol represents 2 watches, so
   $\frac{1}{2}$ a watch symbol represents 2 ÷ 2 = 1 watch.
   Monday has $2\frac{1}{2}$ symbols = 2 + 2 + 1 = 5
   (**1 mark for correct answer**)

   Tuesday has 3 watch symbols, which is more
   than any other day. So Carlos sold the most
   watches on Tuesday.
   (**1 mark for correct answer**)

6. For every 3 screws there are 2 bolts.
   So if there are 3 × 2 = 6 screws
   there are 2 × 2 = 4 bolts.
   (**1 mark for correct answer**)

7. 1 week = 7 days, 2 weeks = 2 × 7 = 14 days.
   So she ran for 14 × 2 = 28 hours.
   (**1 mark for correct answer**)

8. Replace 'number of beehives' with
   4 in the formula. So 4 beehives can make
   4 × 11 = 44 kg of honey.
   (**1 mark for correct answer**)

9. 3 × 7 = 21 (**1 mark for both numbers**)

Test 2 – pages 4-6

1. $1\frac{2}{5} = \frac{5}{5} + \frac{2}{5} = \frac{7}{5}$
   (**1 mark for correct answer**)

2.   9 2 4
   + 8 7 5
     1 7 9 9
         1
   (**1 mark for correct answer**)

3. 0.8 = 0.80 and 0.78 < 0.80,
   so 0.8 should be circled.
   (**1 mark for correct answer**)

4. There are 1000 g in 1 kg, so the rucksack
   weighs 2 × 1000 = 2000 grams.
   (**1 mark for correct answer**)

5. Angles on a straight line add up to 180°,
   so P = 180° − 60° = 120°.
   (**1 mark for correct answer**)

6. 16 (**1 mark**)

7. She has skied 1 km out of 10 km,
   which is $\frac{1}{10}$ of the total distance.
   $\frac{1}{10} = \frac{10}{100} = 10\%$
   (**1 mark for correct answer**)
   Since she has skied 1 km, she has
   10 km − 1 km = 9 km left to ski.
   So she has $\frac{9}{10}$ of the course left to ski.
   (**1 mark for correct answer**)

8. Perimeter of Shape A:
   4 cm + 6 cm + 4 cm + 6 cm = 20 cm
   Perimeter of Shape B:
   4 cm + 4 cm + 4 cm + 4 cm = 16 cm
   So the difference between the perimeters is
   20 cm − 16 cm = 4 cm
   (**2 marks for the correct answer otherwise
   1 mark for one correct perimeter**)

Test 3 – pages 7-9

1.
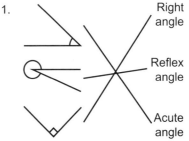

   (**1 mark for all lines correct**)
   Any angle between 90° and 180° is acceptable,
   e.g. 120° (90° and 180° are not suitable
   answers). (**1 mark for correct answer**)

2. $\frac{13}{100} = 13 ÷ 100 = 0.13$
   (**1 mark for correct answer**)

3. It's 3 °C from −3 °C to 0 °C, then 2 °C from
   0 °C to 2 °C, so it's 3 + 2 = 5 °C warmer.
   (**1 mark for correct answer**)

4. The terms increase by 9 − 5 = 4 each time.
   So the sequence is 1, 5, 9, 13, 17
   (**1 mark for both correct**)

5. Cuboid (**1 mark**)

Answers

6. $\frac{3}{5} \xrightarrow{\times 2} \frac{6}{10}$ and $\frac{3}{5} \xrightarrow{\times 3} \frac{9}{15}$

So $\frac{3}{5} \rightarrow \frac{6}{10} \rightarrow \frac{9}{15}$

(1 mark for both correct)

7. The other two sides of the triangle have lengths of 3 cm and 4 cm. So the perimeter is
3 cm + 4 cm + 5 cm = 12 cm
(1 mark for correct answer)

8. 10% of 120 = 120 ÷ 10 = 12 action films.
So he has 120 − 12 = 108 comedy films.
**(2 marks for correct answer otherwise
1 mark for correct working)**

Test 4 – pages 10-12

1.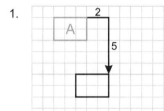

(1 mark)

2. $\frac{7}{12} + \frac{10}{12} = \frac{17}{12} = 1\frac{5}{12}$
(1 mark for correct answer)

3.   4 6 7
   − 1 3 5
   ‾‾‾‾‾
    3 3 2
(1 mark for all missing digits correct)

4.   6 . 5 0
   +   3 . 9 5
   ‾‾‾‾‾‾‾‾
   £ 1 0 . 4 5
        1
(1 mark for correct answer)

      6 .$\overset{4}{\cancel{5}}\overset{1}{0}$
   −   0 . 4 5
   ‾‾‾‾‾‾‾‾
   £ 6 . 0 5
(1 mark for correct answer)

5. Area = length × width = 9 m × 7 m = 63 m²
(1 mark for correct answer)

6. $\frac{7}{10} = \frac{70}{100}$ = 70% were cod.
(1 mark for correct answer)

7. The number of people who don't play a woodwind instrument is 25 − 11 = 14 people.
(1 mark for correct answer)

8. 6 mugs hold the same amount as 2 bottles, so 6 ÷ 2 = 3 mugs hold the same amount as 2 ÷ 2 = 1 bottle.
3 mugs hold 400 ml × 3 = 1200 ml, so one bottle holds 1200 ml.
**(2 marks for correct answer otherwise
1 mark for correct working)**

Test 5 – pages 13-15

1. There are 1000 m in 1 km.
So it is 1300 ÷ 1000 = 1.3 km to the golf course.
(1 mark for correct answer)

2. $\frac{1}{4} = \frac{2}{8}$, so $\frac{3}{8}$ is heavier.
(1 mark for correct answer)

3. Volume of cuboid = Length × Width × Height
= 10 × 2 × 4 = 80 cm³
(1 mark for correct answer)

4.   4 7 1
   ×   6
   ‾‾‾‾‾
   2 8 2 6
        4
So the machine makes 2826 cars in 6 days.
(1 mark for correct answer)

5. $\frac{3}{4} \times \frac{1}{2} = \frac{3}{8}$ **(1 mark)**

6. P is above (1, 2), so its x-coordinate is 1.
It is level with (4, 7), so its y-coordinate is 7.
So the coordinates of P are (1, 7). **(1 mark)**

7. £2 × 16 + £8 = £32 + £8 = £40
(1 mark for correct answer)

$\frac{3}{4}$ × £40 = 3 × 10 = £30
(1 mark for correct answer)

8. Area of rectangle: 4 × 6 = 24 m²
Area of triangle: $\frac{1}{2}$ × 2 × 4 = 4 m²
So the total area of the shape is
24 + 4 = 28 m²
**(2 marks for correct answer otherwise
1 mark for correct working)**

Arithmetic Test – pages 16-17

1. 351 − 100 = 251 **(1 mark)**

2. 14 ÷ 1 = 14 **(1 mark)**

3. 1923 − 1002 = 1923 − 1000 − 2
= 923 − 2
= 921 **(1 mark)**

Answers

4. $3 \times 4 = 12$, $12 \times 5 = 60$ (**1 mark**)

5. $\frac{1}{7} \times \frac{1}{5} = \frac{1 \times 1}{7 \times 5} = \frac{1}{35}$ (**1 mark**)

6. 10% of 400 = 400 ÷ 10 = 40
   20% of 400 = 40 × 2 = 80 (**1 mark**)

7.
   ```
       1 5 9
   ×       4
     6 3 6
     ₂ ₃
   ```
   (**2 marks for correct answer otherwise
   1 mark for correct working**)

8.
   ```
         6 8
   9 )6 ⁶1 ⁷2
   ```
   (**2 marks for correct answer otherwise
   1 mark for correct working**)

Puzzle – page 18

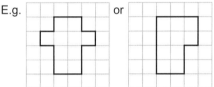

1. A **hexagon** is a six-sided shape.

2. **Parallel** lines are the same distance apart
   and never meet.

3. **Regular** polygons have equal-length sides
   and equal angles.

4. The **circumference** is the outside edge of a
   circle.

5. **Isosceles** triangles have two equal sides
   and two equal angles.

6. A shape with five sides is called a **pentagon**.

7. **Octagon** is the word without a description.
   E.g. 'An octagon is a shape with eight sides.'

Set B

Test 1 – pages 20-22

1. Twenty-seven thousand, four hundred and nine
   (**1 mark**)

2. There are 15 sections, so $\frac{1}{3}$ × 15 = 5 sections
   should be shaded.
   E.g.
   (**1 mark**)

3. £890
   £1740
   (**1 mark for both correct**)

4. Any shape enclosing 10 grid squares.
   E.g.   or
   (**1 mark**)

5. 15, 9, 12 (**1 mark for all correct**)

6. Soup and chips, salad and chips
   (**1 mark for both correct**)

7. 360° − 50° = 310°
   (**1 mark for correct answer**)

8. 10% of 200 = 200 ÷ 10 = 20
   5% of 200 = 20 ÷ 2 = 10
   So 10 should be circled.
   (**1 mark for correct answer**)

9. 5 × 10 = 50 km (**1 mark for correct answer**)
   20 ÷ 10 = 2 cm (**1 mark for correct answer**)

Test 2 – pages 23-25

1. 2260 + 1000 = 3260 words
   (**1 mark for correct answer**)

2. A is a rectangle, B is a parallelogram and C is a
   trapezium. So C should be circled.
   (**1 mark for correct answer**)

   (**1 mark**)

Answers

3.

(**1 mark**)

4. $\frac{1}{20} = \frac{5}{100} = 0.05$
(**1 mark for correct answer**)

5. $180° - 90° - 20° = 70°$
(**1 mark for correct answer**)

6. 70, 10 (**1 mark for both correct**)
70.3 ÷ 9.9 ≈ 70 ÷ 10 = 7,
so 7 should be circled.
(**1 mark for correct answer**)

7. $4 + 6 + 11 + 7 = 28$
$28 ÷ 4 = 7$
(**2 marks for correct answer otherwise
1 mark for correct working**)

Test 3 – pages 26-28

1.
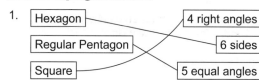

(**1 mark for three correct lines**)

2.
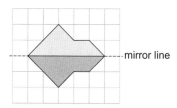
------mirror line

(**1 mark**)

3. 4 kg of wool can make 60 pairs of socks.
12 = 4 × 3, so 12 kg of wool can make
60 × 3 = 180 pairs of socks.
(**1 mark for correct answer**)

4. The 10:00 tram from Lowbury gets to Bullwall
at 10:10 and the 10:55 tram gets to Bullwall at
11:05. She needs to be in Bullwall before 11:00,
so she should get the 10:00 tram.
(**1 mark for correct answer**)

5. $4 × 3 - 2 = 12 - 2 = 10$
$2 + 3 × 2 = 2 + 6 = 8$
$(15 + 5) ÷ 2 = 20 ÷ 2 = 10$
2 + 3 × 2 does not equal 10 so should be circled.
(**1 mark for correct answer**)

6.
```
  1 3 3 r 2
6|8 ²0 ²0
```
There are 133 whole bunches.
(**1 mark for correct answer**)

There are 2 roses left over, so to make another
bunch you'll need 6 – 2 = 4 more.
(**1 mark for correct answer**)

7. $\frac{1}{3} = \frac{4}{12}$, $\frac{1}{6} = \frac{2}{12}$
Smallest to largest: $\frac{1}{6}$, $\frac{1}{3}$, $\frac{5}{12}$
(**1 mark for correct order**)

8. $2 × £2.10 = £4.20$
$3 × £1.50 = £4.50$
So Jon spends £4.20 + £4.50 = £8.70.
He needs £8.70 – £5 = £3.70
more to pay for his order.
(**2 marks for correct answer otherwise
1 mark for working out how much he spent**)

Test 4 – pages 29-31

1. $72.6 - 10 = 62.6$ (**1 mark**)

2. 5 (**1 mark**)
$9 + 5 + 11 + 3 = 28$
(**1 mark for correct answer**)

3. The clock shows 6:15 pm, which is 18:15.
So in one hour it will show 19:15.
(**1 mark for correct answer**)

4. Factors of 20: 1, 2, 4, 5, 10, 20
So 4, 5 and 10 should be circled.
(**1 mark for all circled**)

5. Abe's dad is 47 – 5 = 42 now.
So Abe is 42 ÷ 2 = 21 now.
(**1 mark for correct answer**)

6. For every 1 birch tree there are 3 oak trees.
So 1 in every 4 trees is a birch tree.
As a fraction this is $\frac{1}{4}$.
(**1 mark for correct answer**)

7. Shape Y has been translated 7 units
to the left and 2 units up. (**1 mark**)

8. $\frac{26}{50} = \frac{52}{100} = 52\%$
52% < 62%, so Farrah is further ahead
(**2 marks for correct answer otherwise
1 mark for correct working**)

Answers

Test 5 – pages 32-34

1. 265 ➔ 300
    18 910 ➔ 19 000
    (**1 mark for both correct**)

2. The sector for daisies is twice as large as the sector for lilies, so the first statement is true.
    20 flowers is half of the total. The sector for tulips is smaller than half of the chart, so the second statement is false.
    The sector for sunflowers is half of the chart, so the third statement is false.
    The sectors for tulips and lilies are the same size, so the fourth statement is true.
    So the first and fourth statements should be circled.
    (**1 mark for each true statement circled. Lose 1 mark for each false statement circled.**)

3. 2.63 × 100 = 263 (**1 mark**)

4. 180° − 90° − 60° = 30°
    (**1 mark for correct answer**)

5. $\frac{1}{3}$ of 60 = 20, so she gives away 20 grapes.
    So each friend gets 20 ÷ 4 = 5 grapes.
    (**1 mark for correct answer**)

6. The cube has volume
    3 × 3 × 3 = 9 × 3 = 27 cm³.
    So the difference between the volumes is
    27 − 24 = 3 cm³.
    (**2 marks for correct answer otherwise 1 mark for the correct volume of the cube**)

7. The total poured out of the jug is
    $\frac{2}{5} + \frac{3}{10} = \frac{4}{10} + \frac{3}{10} = \frac{7}{10}$ litre.
    So the amount left in the jug is
    $1 - \frac{7}{10} = \frac{10}{10} - \frac{7}{10} = \frac{3}{10}$ litre.
    (**2 marks for correct answer otherwise 1 mark for correct working**)

Arithmetic Test – pages 35-36

1. 9032 + 2000 = 11 032 (**1 mark**)

2. 18 × 5 = 90 (**1 mark**)

3. $\frac{4}{6} + \frac{1}{6} = \frac{5}{6}$ (**1 mark**)

4. 36.5 × 10 = 365 (**1 mark**)

5. $\frac{1}{8}$ of 32 = 32 ÷ 8 = 4 (**1 mark**)

6. 0.3 + 4.6 = 4.9 (**1 mark**)

7.
$$
\begin{array}{r}
7\ 9\ 3 \\
\times\ \ \ 1\ 4 \\
\hline
3\ 1\ 7\ 2 \\
7\ 9\ 3\ 0 \\
\hline
1\ 1\ 1\ 0\ 2 \\
\end{array}
$$
    (**2 marks for correct answer otherwise 1 mark for correct working**)

8.
$$4\overline{)3\ {}^{3}0\ {}^{2}3\ {}^{3}6}\quad = 759$$
    (**2 marks for correct answer otherwise 1 mark for correct working**)

Puzzle – page 37

Peter: 6 × 12 = 72,
      32 ÷ 4 = 8,
      7 × 8 = 56,
      81 ÷ 9 = 9
      72 + 8 + 56 + 9 = 145

Yasmin: 66 ÷ 11 = 6,
       9 × 7 = 63,
       54 ÷ 6 = 9,
       8 × 12 = 96
       6 + 63 + 9 + 96 = 174

So Peter gets a **skeleton key** and Yasmin gets a **fairy wand**.

Answers

Set C

Test 1 – pages 39-41

1. 188 > 181
   3921 < 3995
   (**1 mark for both correct**)

2. Each dash represents 0.1 litres.
   The water is at the third dash above 1 litre,
   so there are 1.3 litres of water in the kettle.
   (**1 mark for correct answer**)

3.
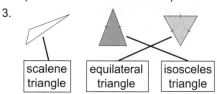

   (**1 mark for three correct lines**)

4. It's 8 °C from –8 °C to 0 °C, then 1 °C from 0 °C
   to 1 °C. So the difference between –8 °C and
   1 °C is 8 + 1 = 9 °C.
   (**1 mark for correct answer**)

5. To get from 12 mins 40 seconds to 13 mins you
   need 20 seconds. To get from 13 mins to
   15 mins you need 2 mins. So Leanne needs to
   bake her cake for another 2 mins 20 seconds.
   (**1 mark for correct answer**)

6.
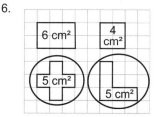

   (**1 mark for correct answer**)

7. 19 ÷ 7 = 2 remainder 5
   So $\frac{19}{7}$ = $2\frac{5}{7}$ (**1 mark for correct answer**)

8.
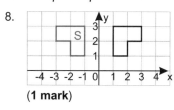

   (**1 mark**)

9. Hiro pays £2.99 = 299p.
   Isla pays 4p × 60 = 240p.
   So Hiro pays 299 − 240 = 59p more.
   (**2 marks for correct answer otherwise
   1 mark for correct multiplication**)

Test 2 – pages 42-44

1. Point 1 = (2, 3), Point 2 = (6, 3), Point 3 = (4, 6)
   (**1 mark for all three correct**)

2. 0.65 km = 650 m.
   680 > 650, so Leanne runs further.
   (**1 mark for correct answer**)

3. Log Flume tickets: 5 × £2 = £10
   Ferris Wheel tickets: 3 × £5 = £15
   Total cost = £10 + £15 = £25
   (**1 mark for correct answer**)

4. 1274 ÷ 98 or 1274 ÷ 13
   (**1 mark for one correct division**)

5. There are 1000 ml in 1 litre,
   so there are 0.5 × 1000 = 500 ml in a bottle.
   500 ÷ 20 = 50 ÷ 2 = 25 drinks
   (**2 marks for correct answer otherwise
   1 mark for correct working**)

6. 100% − 25% = 75% of customers
   don't have blonde hair. 75% = $\frac{75}{100}$ = $\frac{3}{4}$
   (**1 mark for correct answer**)

7. Area of triangle: $\frac{1}{2}$ × 4 × 4 = 2 × 4 = 8 cm²
   Area of square: 3 × 3 = 9 cm²
   So the difference in area is 9 − 8 = 1 cm²
   (**2 marks for correct answer otherwise
   1 mark for one correct area**)

8. There are three options where A × B = 12:
   1 × 12, 2 × 6 or 3 × 4
   Add each option to see which adds to 8:
   1 + 12 = 13, 2 + 6 = 8 and 3 + 4 = 7
   So the answer is A = 2, B = 6 (or A = 6, B = 2)
   (**1 mark for correct answer**)

Answers

Test 3 – pages 45-47

1. The radius is half of the diameter, so the radius of the circle is 6 ÷ 2 = 3 mm.
(**1 mark for correct answer**)

2. 59 m (**1 mark**)

3.
```
      1 7 4 0
    ×     1 2
      3 4 8 0
         1
    1 7 4 0 0
  £ 2 0 8 8 0
      1
```
(**2 marks for correct answer otherwise 1 mark for correct working**)

4. 1 hexagon = 6 points.
$\frac{1}{2}$ a hexagon = 6 ÷ 2 = 3 points.
Leanne has 6 + 6 + 6 + 6 + 3 = 27 points.
Isla has 6 + 6 = 12 points.
So Leanne has 27 – 12 = 15 more points.
(**1 mark for correct answer**)

5. $\frac{1}{5}$ of 40 = 40 ÷ 5 = 8
$\frac{3}{5}$ of 40 = 8 × 3 = 24
So Leanne has read 24 pages.
(**1 mark for correct answer**)

6. 10% of 300 = 300 ÷ 10 = 30
60% of 300 = 30 × 6 = 180
So 180 of the fossils are dinosaur fossils.
(**1 mark for correct answer**)

7. 30 ÷ 5 = 6, so there are 6 lots of 5 miles in 30. The distance in km will be 6 lots of 8 km, which is 6 × 8 = 48 km.
(**1 mark for correct answer**)

8. 1 hour = 60 minutes
6 hours = 60 × 6 = 360 minutes
360 ÷ 10 = 36
So it took the artist 36 days to complete the painting.
(**2 marks for correct answer otherwise 1 mark for correct working**)

Test 4 – pages 48-50

1. 6.4 and 3.6
(**1 mark for both correct**)

2. A = 45° (**1 mark for answer between 44° and 46° inclusive**)

3. £3.20 × 100 = £320
£320 × 3 = £960
(**1 mark for correct answer**)
£3.20 × 3 = £9.60
£10 − £9.60 = £0.40 = 40p
(**1 mark for correct answer**)

4. M = 1000, X = 10, I = 1
1000 + 1000 + 10 + 1 = 2011
(**1 mark for correct answer**)

5.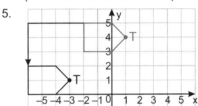
(**1 mark**)
T = (−3, 1) (**1 mark**)

6. Volume = length × width × height
10 × 5 × 4 = 50 × 4 = 200 cm³
(**1 mark for correct answer**)

7. She starts with 5 × 6 = 30 apple slices.
30 − 9 = 21, so she has $\frac{21}{6}$ = $3\frac{3}{6}$ = $3\frac{1}{2}$ apples left.
(**2 marks for correct answer otherwise 1 mark for correct working**)

Test 5 – pages 51-53

1. For every pentagon there are 3 triangles.
(**1 mark**)

2. 30, 22, 14, 6, −2 (**1 mark for all correct**)

3.
```
        2 1 1
  25 ⎞5 ⁵2 ²7 ²5
```
211 whole boxes can be filled.
(**2 marks for correct answer otherwise 1 mark for correct working**)

4. 5 faces, 8 edges, 5 vertices
(**1 mark for all correct**)

Answers

5. Find 3 miles on the vertical axis and go across to the line. Then go down to the axis and read the cost. The line down from 3 miles is halfway between £2 and £3, so the journey would cost £2.50.
   (**1 mark for correct answer**)

6. 9, 15, 24 and 30 are multiples of 3.
   5, 15 and 30 are multiples of 5.
   So 15 and 30 should be circled
   (**1 mark for both correct**)

7. Find the missing length:

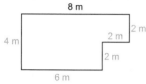

   Perimeter: 8 + 2 + 2 + 2 + 6 + 4 = 24 m
   The length of the hedge is the perimeter, so the hedge is 24 m long.
   (**1 mark for correct answer**)

8.

	⬡	▽
Pair 1	1	10
Pair 2	2	7
Pair 3	3	4
Pair 4	4	1

   (**2 marks for all correct values otherwise 1 mark for at least 2 correct values**)

Arithmetic Test – pages 54-55

1. 2000 + 600 + 30 = 2630 (**1 mark**)

2. 18.5 − 8.3 = 10.2 (**1 mark**)

3. $5^2 = 5 \times 5 = 25$ (**1 mark**)

4. 490 ÷ 7 = 70 (**1 mark**)

5. $\dfrac{4}{5} \div 3 = \dfrac{4}{5 \times 3} = \dfrac{4}{15}$ (**1 mark**)

6. $\dfrac{2}{7} = \dfrac{4}{14}$

   $\dfrac{1}{14} + \dfrac{4}{14} = \dfrac{5}{14}$ (**1 mark**)

7.
$$
\begin{array}{r}
2\ 7\ 3\ 1 \\
\times \quad 2\ 2 \\
\hline
5\ 4\ 6\ 2 \\
5\ 4\ 6\ 2\ 0 \\
\hline
6\ 0\ 0\ 8\ 2 \\
\end{array}
$$
   (**2 marks for correct answer otherwise 1 mark for correct working**)

8.
$$
12\overline{)4\,^4 9\,^1 9\,^7 2}
$$
   4 1 6
   (**2 marks for correct answer otherwise 1 mark for correct working**)

Puzzle – page 56

	Start Time	End Time
Hidden Compass	15:00	15:30
Rapid River	15:30	16:15
Cursed Quicksand	16:15	18:15
Perilous Vines	18:15	19:30
Holy Hill	19:30	22:30
Secret Temple	22:30	Midnight

Progress Chart

You've finished all the tests in the book — well done!

Now it's time to put your scores in here
and see how you've done.

	Set A	Set B	Set C
Test 1			
Test 2			
Test 3			
Test 4			
Test 5			
Arithmetic Test			
Total			

See if you're on target by checking your marks for each set in the table below.

Mark	
0-29	You're not quite there yet — keep going back over the questions you find tricky and you'll improve your maths skills in no time.
30-45	You're getting there — good effort! Keep working on the topics you struggle with until you're really happy with them.
46-60	Give yourself a huge pat on the back — you've mastered this Foundation book! If you're ready to try something as hard as the real SATs, have a look at our Book 1 and Book 2 10-Minute Tests.